Why Mone

Research has shown that repetition is essential for the brain to learn and recall information. The engaging activities in this book will provide your child with repeated practice of grade-level-appropriate vocabulary and math skills about money. This kind of practice helps develop fluency and build a strong foundation in mathematical thinking and reasoning, an important skill for academic success.

Teaching children about money involves teaching what money is, the denominations of currency, how to count money, why money is important, and how money is used in everyday life. Teaching children the denominations of coins and bills leads naturally to counting exercises. After children can add and subtract the value of coins and bills, they can learn about saving money and using money to make purchases.

Upon your child's completion of each activity, use the provided incentive chart and stickers to track progress and celebrate your child's success.

SKILLS

- Identifying coins and bills, by name, image, and value
- Coin combinations to one dollar
- Counting combinations of coins and bills to five dollars
- Making change
- Identifying money equivalencies
- Problem solving

HOW YOU CAN HELP SUPPORT LEARNING

- Work with your child in a quiet, calm setting.
- Complete some activities together. Keep a positive attitude and provide words of encouragement to support your child's journey in becoming a lifelong learner.
- Provide coins and bills if needed to help your child complete the activities.
- Help your child learn the basic concept of using money to buy items through role playing with real or play money in a store situation.
- Make trips to the grocery store or restaurant a learning experience by allowing your child to help count the amount of money to pay.

Shiny Pennies

Count the pennies and write the amount.

Count pennies by 1s. 1 penny is one cent.

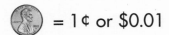 = 1¢ or $0.01

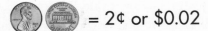 = 2¢ or $0.02

100 pennies = $1.00

1

_____ 3 ¢

2

_____ 7 ¢

3

_____ 9 ¢

4

_____ 11 ¢

5

_____ 2 ¢

6

_____ 20 ¢

Penny's Piggy Bank

Color the path of pennies to help Penny find her piggy bank.

My Piggy Bank

Write the number that shows how much money is in each piggy bank.

I have _____ ¢.

I have _____ ¢.

I have _____ ¢.

I have _____ ¢.

Pirate's Treasure

Count the coins to help the pirate find the treasure chest.
Write the total beside the chest.

_____ ¢

Nifty Nickels

Count by **5s** to find the amount. Write the amount counted on each line.

Count nickels by 5s. 1 nickel is 5 cents.

 = 5¢ or $0.05

    = 25¢ or

    5   10   15   20   25 = $0.25

___5___ ___10___ _____   _____¢

_____ _____ _____ _____ _____   _____¢

Count the amount.

_____ _____ _____ _____   _____¢

_____ _____ _____ _____ _____   _____¢

What's in the Safe?

Write how much money is in each safe.

 1

_____ ¢

 2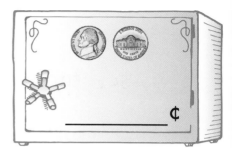

_____ ¢

 3

_____ ¢

 4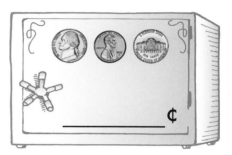

_____ ¢

 5

_____ ¢

 6

_____ ¢

 7

_____ ¢

 8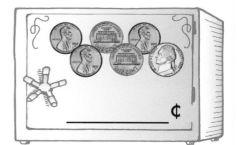

_____ ¢

How Much Money?

Color the amount of money you will need to buy each object.

1

1¢

2

4¢

3

5¢

4

6¢

5

10¢

6

15¢

Counting Dimes

Count by **10s** to find the amount. Write the amount counted on each line.

Count dimes by 10s. 1 dime is 10 cents.

= 10¢ or $0.10

= 50¢
or
= $0.50

10   20   30   40   50

_10_ _20_ _____ _____   _____ ¢

_____ _____ _____ _____ _____ _____   _____ ¢

Count the amount.

_____ _____ _____ _____   _____ ¢

_____ _____ _____ _____ _____ _____   _____ ¢

How Much Money?

Count by **10s** along the path to help the boy find out how much the cap costs. Write the amount.

$ _____

Matching Coin Sets

Draw a line from each coin purse to the wallet that has the same amount of money.

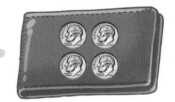

Quarters

Count by **25s** to find the amount. Write the amount counted on each line.

> ## Count quarters by 25s. 1 quarter is 25 cents.
>
> $= 25¢$ or $0.25
>
> $= 50¢$ or $0.50
>
>
>
> 25   50   75   100   125
>
> 5 quarters = $1.25

25   50   ____   _____ ¢

____   ____   ____   ____ $_____

Count the amount.

____   ____   ____   ____   ____   _____ ¢

____   ____   ____   ____   ____   _____ ¢

Grocery Shopping

Color the money you will need to buy each item.

1

12¢

2

30¢

3

Butter 52¢

4

46¢

5

29¢

6

31¢

Three in a Row

Circle three coins in a row that equal the amount on each price tag.

12¢

20¢

27¢

55¢

Money Patterns

Circle the item that comes next in each pattern.

Quick Quiz

Fill in the bubble that shows the correct amount.

3¢   4¢   5¢

○   ○   ○

1¢   10¢   25¢

○   ○   ○

2¢   5¢   10¢

○   ○   ○

4¢   22¢   14¢

○   ○   ○

3¢   15¢   30¢

○   ○   ○

50¢   60¢   65¢

○   ○   ○

Piggy Savings

Write the amount of money in each piggy bank.

1. _____ ¢

2. _____ ¢

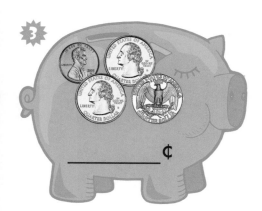

3. _____ ¢

4. _____ ¢

5. _____ ¢

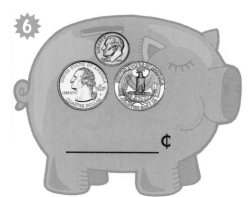

6. _____ ¢

Matching Money Bags

Draw a line to match the money bags that have equal amounts of money in them.

1

2

3

4

5

Even Amounts

Write the amount of the coins in each box. Then circle the
even amounts to help the bee get to the hive.

_____ ¢	_____ ¢
_____ ¢	_____ ¢	_____ ¢
_____ ¢	_____ ¢	_____ ¢
_____ ¢	_____ ¢	_____ ¢
_____ ¢	_____ ¢	

Counting Quarters

Count the quarters and write each amount.

  _____ ¢

   _____ ¢

    _____ ¢

     $_____

      $_____

       $_____

Do I Have Enough?

Cross out the coins that add up to the amount on each price tag.

 32¢ =

 56¢ =

 76¢ =

 47¢ =

 90¢ =

 88¢ =

Bills

Count and write the amount for each.

 = $1.00

= $5.00

 = $10.00

10   15   16

---

1   2   3   4 $___4___.00

_____   _____   _____ $_____.00

_____   _____   _____   _____ $_____.00

_____   _____   _____ $_____.00

_____   _____   _____   _____ $_____.00

Coins and Bills

Draw lines to match the coins with their name and amount.

quarter   •   •  •   • 10¢

nickel   •   •   •   • 25¢

dime   •   •   •   • 5¢

Count and write the amount for each.

$_____ . _____ _____

↑ dollars   ↑ cents   ↑

$1.00 $1.25 $1.26 $ _1_ . 26

_____ _____ _____ $ _____ . _____

_____ _____ _____ $ _____ . _____

Adding Money

Count and write the amount for each.

<u>25</u> <u>50</u> _____ _____ _____ _____ ¢

_____ _____ _____ _____ _____ _____ ¢

_____ _____ _____ _____ _____ _____ ¢

_____ _____ _____ _____ $_____ . _____

_____ _____ _____ $_____ . _____

24

© 2012 CTP - 7221

Money Match

Fill in the bubble to show the correct answer.

1 How much is this?

37¢	60¢	62¢
○	○	○

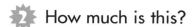

2 How much is this?

40¢	51¢	61¢
○	○	○

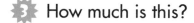

3 How much is this?

$10	$1	$5
○	○	○

4 How much is this?

$6.28	$10	$10.28
○	○	○

5 Bob has 34¢.
He spends 22¢ on .
How much money is left?

46¢	22¢	12¢
○	○	○

Smallest to Biggest

Write the amount of each group of coins.
Then write the letters on the lines to answer the question below.

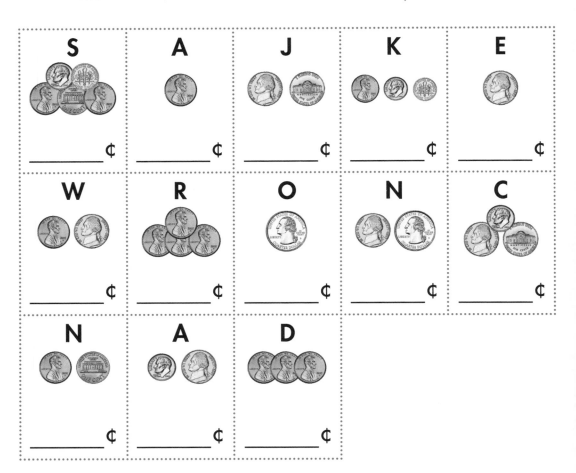

S	A	J	K	E
_____ ¢	_____ ¢	_____ ¢	_____ ¢	_____ ¢

W	R	O	N	C
_____ ¢	_____ ¢	_____ ¢	_____ ¢	_____ ¢

N	A	D
_____ ¢	_____ ¢	_____ ¢

Which president's picture is on the $20 bill?

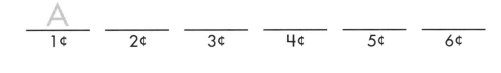

A ___ ___ ___ ___ ___ ___
1¢   2¢   3¢   4¢   5¢   6¢

___ ___ ___ ___ ___ ___ ___
10¢   15¢   20¢   21¢   23¢   25¢   30¢

Shopping Trip

Circle the answer for each question.

1 Do you have enough to buy this?   **yes   no**

         30¢

2 Do you have enough to buy this?   **yes   no**

         42¢

3 Do you have enough to buy this?   **yes   no**

          75¢

4 Do you have enough to buy this?   **yes   no**

           37¢

Money Problems

Add or subtract to solve the problems.

1 You have 32¢. You earn 45¢ more.
How much do you have altogether?

$$\begin{array}{r} 32¢ \\ +\quad 45¢ \\ \hline ¢ \end{array}$$

2 You have 45¢. You spend 31¢.
How much do you have left?

$$\begin{array}{r} ¢ \\ -\quad ¢ \\ \hline ¢ \end{array}$$

3 Ann gave you 50¢. You give 30¢ back.
How much do you still have?

$$\begin{array}{r} ¢ \\ -\quad ¢ \\ \hline ¢ \end{array}$$

4 You have 96¢. You spend 34¢.
How much do you have left?

$$\begin{array}{r} ¢ \\ -\quad ¢ \\ \hline ¢ \end{array}$$

5 Joe has 24¢. He finds 63¢ more.
How much does he have now?

$$\begin{array}{r} ¢ \\ +\quad ¢ \\ \hline ¢ \end{array}$$

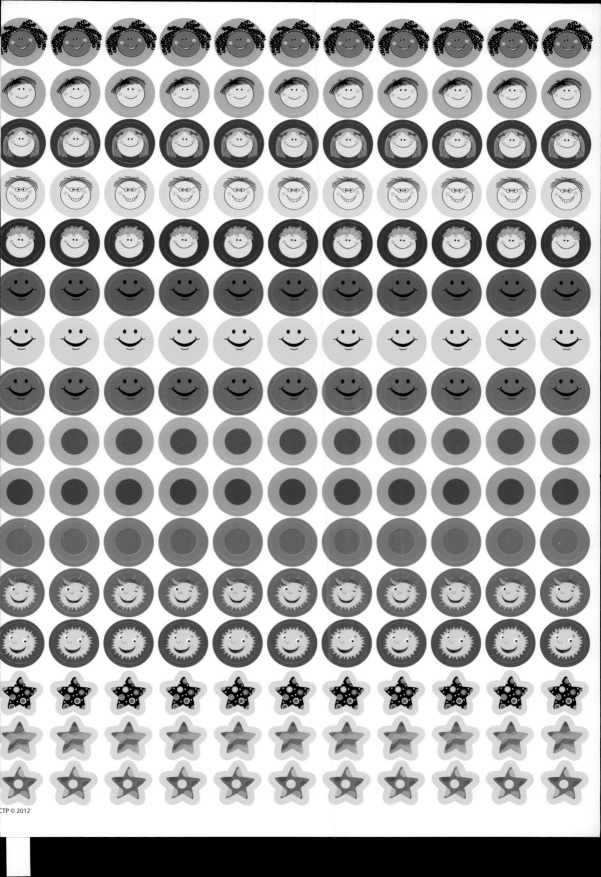

The Sports Shop

Draw lines to match the items to the money needed to buy them.

Coin Crossword

Write the names of the coins to solve the crossword puzzle.

Across

1

3

5

Word Box

penny   half-dollar   dime

nickel   quarter

Down

2

4

© 2012 CTP - 7221

Please Pay

Cross out the coins that add up to the amount on each price tag.

 **1** 42¢ =

 2 66¢ =

 3 96¢ =

 4 57¢ =

 5 $1.00 =

 6 28¢ =

Piggy Bank Match

Cross out the coins that equal the amount shown for each.

40¢

1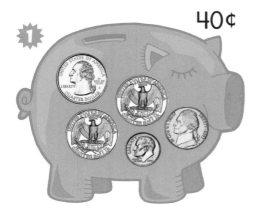

24¢

2

55¢

3

17¢

4

75¢

5

38¢

6

Three in a Row

Circle three coins in a row that equal the amount on each price tag.

16¢

40¢

60¢

51¢

How Much Does It Cost?

Use the prices for each item to answer the questions below.

Phone	$1.25
Shovel	$2.00
Socks	$1.35

Sunglasses	$1.00
Teddy Bear	$2.15
Tie	$1.80

1 How much will the bear
and the tie cost?

$.
+ $.
$

2 How much will the shovel
and the phone cost?

$.
+ $.
$

3 How much will the sunglasses
and the socks cost?

$.
+ $.
$

4 How much will the phone
and the sunglasses cost?

$.
+ $.
$

The Pet Shop

Draw lines to match the pets to the money needed to buy them.

At the Toy Store

Look at the prices of the toys and solve the problems.

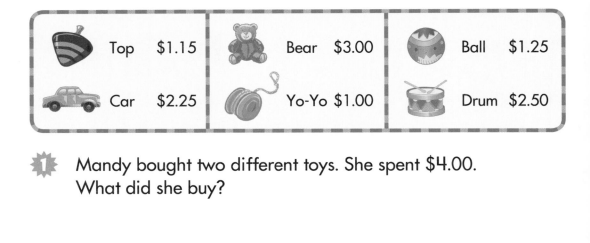

Top $1.15

Car $2.25

Bear $3.00

Yo-Yo $1.00

Ball $1.25

Drum $2.50

1   Mandy bought two different toys. She spent $4.00.
What did she buy?

_____ , _____

2   Brian bought two different toys. He spent $3.65.
What did he buy?

_____ , _____

3   Nikki and Brandon each bought a toy. Nikki's toy cost
$1.00 less than Brandon's toy. What did each child buy?

Nikki _____   Brandon _____

4   Scott has $3.00. He will buy two different toys.
What are the two most expensive toys he can buy?

_____ , _____

Money Mania Word Search

Find and circle the words from the Word Box.

money	coin	dollar	cent
penny	nickel	dime	quarter

t	p	u	q	h	w	m	j	d	t
o	e	h	h	w	n	c	h	o	g
e	n	m	o	n	e	y	l	l	g
w	n	d	b	p	d	m	m	l	q
c	y	i	y	t	l	d	b	a	u
o	f	m	x	m	n	u	c	r	a
i	b	e	k	d	s	m	a	h	r
n	d	q	s	c	e	n	t	t	t
b	j	p	y	o	q	y	n	d	e
y	t	n	i	c	k	e	l	g	r

What Do I Owe?

Cross out the coins you will need to buy each item.

1

2

3

4

5

6

7

8

What Equals a Dollar?

1 How many equal a dollar? _____

2 How many equal a dollar? _____

3 How many equal a dollar? _____

4 How many equal a dollar? _____

5 How many equal a dollar? _____

In the box, draw a combination of coins that equal a dollar.

Quick Quiz

Fill in the bubble to show the correct answer.

1 How much is this?

87¢	60¢	62¢
○	○	○

2 How much is this worth?

$10	$1	$5
○	○	○

3 How much is this?

$6.28	$10	$10.28
○	○	○

4 How much is this?

$3.24

+ $4.12

$7.36	$7.32	$1.12
○	○	○

5 Sam has 46¢. She spends

22¢ on .

How much money is left?

46¢	24¢	12¢
○	○	○

Change, Please!

Answer each question by writing the correct amount of change on the lines.

Megan has $1.00

1 If Megan buys a

 50¢

how much change
will she get? _____

2 If she buys a

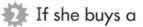 75¢

how much change
will she get? _____

3 If she buys a

 $1.00

how much change
will she get? _____

4 If she buys a

 25¢

how much change
will she get? _____

5 If she buys a

 60¢

how much change
will she get? _____

6 If she buys a

 45¢

how much change
will she get? _____

7 If she buys a

 15¢

how much change
will she get? _____

8 If she buys a

 30¢

how much change
will she get? _____

More Money

Count the money and write the amount for each.

_____

_____

_____

_____

_____

_____

Do You Have Enough?

Circle the answer to each question.

 Do you have enough to buy this?   **yes**   **no**

 Do you have enough to buy this?   **yes**   **no**

 Do you have enough to buy this?   **yes**   **no**

 Do you have enough to buy this?   **yes**   **no**

Total It Up

Write the total amount the two items would cost together.

 $1.25    $1.50

_____

 50¢    26¢

_____

 $8.50    $7.00

_____

 $5.50    $4.00

_____

How Much Money?

Count and write the amount.

_____ _____ _____ _____ _____ _____ ¢

_____ _____ _____ _____ _____ _____ ¢

_____ _____ _____ _____ $_____ . _____

_____ _____ _____ _____ $_____ . _____

_____ _____ _____ $_____ . _____

© 2012 CTP - 7221

The Robot Store

Look at the prices of the robots to answer the questions below.

$1.50 $2.00 $3.25 $2.50

1   2   3   4

1 Which robot costs the most? _____

2 Which robot costs the least? _____

3 How much more does Robot #4 cost than Robot #1? _____

4 How much would it cost to buy Robot #2 and #3? _____

5 How much would it cost to buy Robot #1 and #4? _____

Lunchtime

Use the menu to write how much the items cost
and how much change each child received.

MENU

Apple 30¢	Hot Dog $1.35	French Fries 80¢
Banana 25¢	Sandwich $1.95	Milk 45¢
	Hamburger $2.25	

1 Mia had $3.00. She bought a sandwich and milk.

cost _____   change _____

2 Kevin had $4.00. He bought a hamburger and french fries.

cost _____   change _____

3 Carly had $1.00. She bought an apple and two bananas.

cost _____   change _____

4 Devon had $2.75. He bought two hot dogs.

cost _____   change _____

5 Jacob had $5.00. He bought a hamburger, a hot dog
and french fries.

cost _____   change _____

Toy Snakes

Write **<** or **>** to show which toy snake costs more.

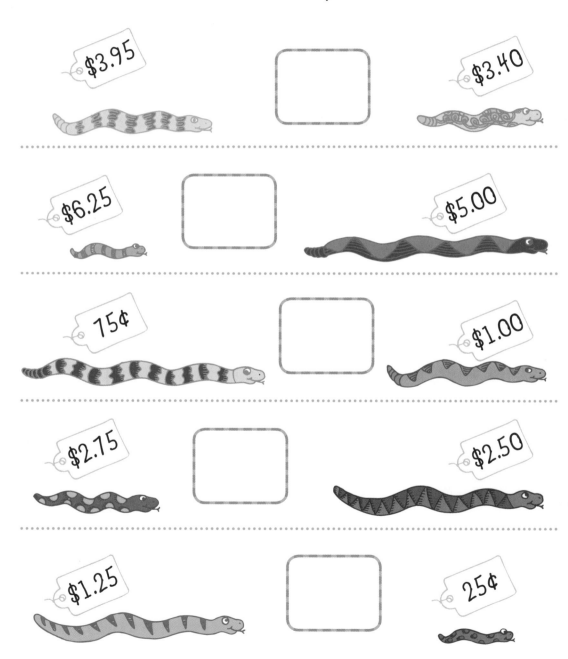

$3.95   [ ] $3.40

$6.25   [ ] $5.00

75¢   [ ] $1.00

$2.75   [ ] $2.50

$1.25   [ ]   25¢

Money

Count the money and write the amount for each.

_____

_____

_____

_____

_____

_____

Heads or Tails?

Write **penny**, **nickel**, **dime**, or **quarter** and its value next to each coin.

_____   _____ ¢

_____   _____ ¢

_____   _____ ¢

_____   _____ ¢

_____   _____ ¢

_____   _____ ¢

_____   _____ ¢

_____   _____ ¢

If You Had $100

Draw a picture of what you would buy if you had $100.

Answer Key

PAGE 2

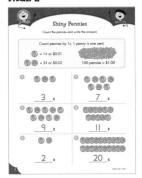

Shiny Pennies

Count the pennies and write the amount.

Count pennies by 1s. 1 penny is one cent.
= 1¢ or $0.01
= 2¢ or $0.02   100 pennies = $1.00

1. 3 ¢
2. 7 ¢
3. 9 ¢
4. 11 ¢
5. 2 ¢
6. 20 ¢

PAGE 3

Penny's Piggy Bank

Color the path of pennies to help Penny find her piggy bank.

PAGE 4

My Piggy Bank

Write the number that shows how much money is in each piggy bank.

1. I have 7 ¢
2. I have 8 ¢
3. I have 10 ¢
4. I have 12 ¢

PAGE 5

Pirate's Treasure

Count the coins to help the pirate find the treasure chest.
Write the total beside the chest.

20 ¢

PAGE 6

Nifty Nickels

Count by 5s to find the amount. Write the amount counted on each line.

Count nickels by 5s. 1 nickel is 5 cents.
= 5¢ or $0.05   = 25¢ or
        5 10 15 20 25   = $0.25

5 10 15   15 ¢
5 10 15 20 25   25 ¢

Count the amount.

5 10 15 16   16 ¢
5 10 11 12 13   13 ¢

PAGE 7

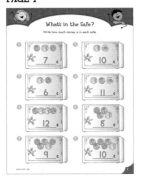

What's in the Safe?

Write how much money is in each safe.

1. 7 ¢
2. 10 ¢
3. 6 ¢
4. 11 ¢
5. 12 ¢
6. 8 ¢
7. 9 ¢
8. 10 ¢

PAGE 8

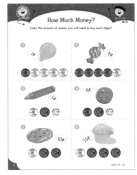

How Much Money?

Color the amount of money you will need to buy each object.

1. 1¢
2. 4¢
3. 5¢
4. 9¢
5. 10¢
6. 15¢

PAGE 9

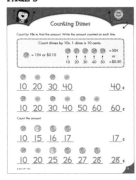

Counting Dimes

Count by 10s to find the amount. Write the amount counted on each line.

= 10¢ or $0.10   = 50¢
        10 20 30 40 50   or = $0.50

10 20 30 40   40¢
10 20 30 40 50 60   60 ¢

Count the amount.

10 15 16 17   17 ¢
10 20 25 26 27 28   28 ¢

PAGE 10

How Much Money?

Count by 10s along the path to help the boy find out how much the cap costs.
Write the amount.

$ 1.20

PAGE 11

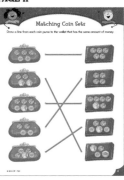

Matching Coin Sets

Draw a line from each coin purse to the wallet that has the same amount of money.

PAGE 12

Quarters

Count by 25s to find the amount. Write the amount counted on each line.

= 25¢ or $0.25
= 50¢ or $0.50   25 50 75 100 125
                   5 quarters = $1.25

25 50 75   75 ¢
25 50 75 1.00 $ 1.00

Count the amount.

25 35 40 41 42   42 ¢
25 50 60 65 70   70 ¢

PAGE 13

Grocery Shopping

Color the money you will need to buy each item.

1. 12¢
2. 30¢
3. 52¢
4. 46¢
5. 29¢
6. 31¢

PAGE 14

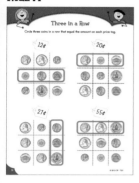

PAGE 15

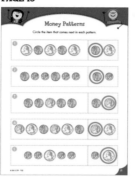

PAGE 16

PAGE 17

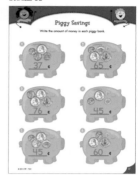

PAGE 18

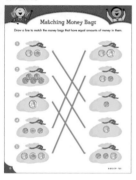

PAGE 19

PAGE 20

PAGE 21

PAGE 22

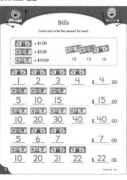

PAGE 23

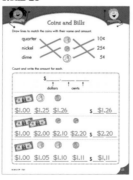

PAGE 24

PAGE 25

Smallest to Biggest

Write the amount of each group of coins.
Then write the letters on the lines to answer the question below.

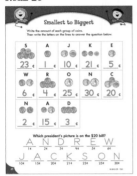

S	A	J	K	E
23¢	1¢	10¢	21¢	5¢

W	R	O	N	C
6¢	4¢	25¢	30¢	20¢

N	A	D		
2¢	15¢	3¢		

Which president's picture is on the $20 bill?

A N D R E W
14¢ 1¢ 3¢ 4¢ 5¢ 6¢

J A C K S O N
10¢ 1¢ 20¢ 21¢ 23¢ 25¢ 30¢

Shopping Trip

Circle the answer for each question.

1. Do you have enough to buy this? yes **no** — 30¢
2. Do you have enough to buy this? **yes** no — 42¢
3. Do you have enough to buy this? yes **no** — 75¢
4. Do you have enough to buy this? **yes** no — 37¢

Money Problems

Add or subtract to solve the problems.

1. You have 32¢. You earn 45¢ more.
   How much do you have altogether?
   32¢
   + 45¢
   77¢

2. You have 45¢. You spend 31¢.
   How much do you have left?
   45¢
   − 31¢
   14¢

3. Ann gave you 50¢. You give 30¢ back.
   How much do you still have?
   50¢
   − 30¢
   20¢

4. You have 96¢. You spend 34¢.
   How much do you have left?
   96¢
   − 34¢
   62¢

5. Joe has 24¢. He finds 63¢ more.
   How much does he have now?
   24¢
   + 63¢
   87¢

The Sports Shop

Draw lines to match the items to the money needed to buy them.

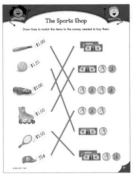

$1.00
$1.25
$1.00
$1.50
$1.50
75¢

Coin Crossword

Write the names of the coins to solve the crossword puzzle.

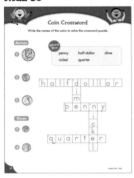

Across

penny   half-dollar   dime
nickel   quarter

h a l f d o l l a r
d i m e
p e n n y
n i c k e l

Down

q u a r t e r

Please Pay

Cross out the coins that add up to the amount on each price tag.

1. 42¢
2. 66¢
3. 96¢
4. 57¢
5. $1.00
6. 28¢

Piggy Bank Match

Cross out the coins that equal the amount shown for each.

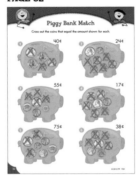

1. 40¢
2. 24¢
3. 55¢
4. 17¢
5. 75¢
6. 38¢

Three in a Row

Circle three coins in a row that equal the amount on each price tag.

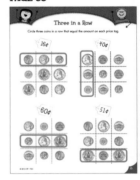

16¢
40¢
60¢
51¢

How Much Does It Cost?

Use the prices for each item to answer the questions below.

Phone	$1.25	Sunglasses	$1.00
Shovel	$2.00	Teddy Bear	$2.15
Socks	$1.35	Tie	$1.80

1. How much will the bear and the tie cost?
   $ 2.15
   + $ 1.80
   $ 3.95

2. How much will the shovel and the phone cost?
   $ 2.00
   + $ 1.25
   $ 3.25

3. How much will the sunglasses and the socks cost?
   $ 1.00
   + $ 1.35
   $ 2.35

4. How much will the phone and the sunglasses cost?
   $ 1.25
   + $ 1.00
   $ 2.25

The Pet Shop

Draw lines to match the pets to the money needed to buy them.

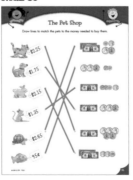

$2.25
$1.75
$2.15
$1.35
$2.65
95¢

At the Toy Store

Look at the prices of the toys and solve the problems.

| Top | $1.15 | Bear | $3.00 | Ball | $1.25 |
| Car | $2.25 | Yo-Yo | $1.00 | Drum | $2.50 |

1. Mandy bought two different toys. She spent $4.00.
   What did she buy?
   Bear   Yo-Yo

2. Brian bought two different toys. He spent $3.65.
   What did he buy?
   Top   Drum

3. Nikki and Brandon each bought a toy. Nikki's toy cost $1.00 less than Brandon's toy. What did each child buy?
   Nikki **Ball**   Brandon **Car**

4. Scott has $3.00. He will buy two different toys.
   What are the two most expensive toys he can buy?
   Top   Ball

Money Mania Word Search

Find and circle the words from the Word Box.

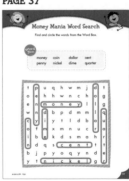

money   coin   dollar   cent
penny   nickel   dime   quarter

PAGE 38

What Do I Owe?

Cross out the coins you will need to buy each item.

1. 15¢
2. 70¢
3. 30¢
4. 55¢
5. 50¢
6. 65¢
7. 85¢
8. 90¢

PAGE 39

What Equals a Dollar?

1. How many ____ equal a dollar? **100**
2. How many ____ equal a dollar? **20**
3. How many ____ equal a dollar? **10**
4. How many ____ equal a dollar? **4**
5. How many ____ equal a dollar? **2**

In the box, draw a combination of coins that equal a dollar.

Answer will vary

PAGE 40

Quick Quiz

Fill in the bubble to show the correct answer.

1. How much is this? 87¢ ○ 60¢ ○ 62¢ ○
2. How much is this worth? $10 ● $1 ○ $5 ○
3. How much is this? $6.28 ● $10 ○ $10.28 ○
4. How much is this?
   $3.24
   + $4.12 $7.36 ● $7.32 ○ $1.12 ○
5. Sam has 46¢. She spends 22¢ on ____. How much money is left? 46¢ ○ 24¢ ● 12¢ ○

PAGE 41

Change, Please!

Answer each question by writing the correct amount of change on the lines.

Megan has $1.00

1. If Megan buys a 50¢, how much change will she get? **50¢**
2. If she buys a 15¢, how much change will she get? **25¢**
3. If she buys a $1.00, how much change will she get? **0**
4. If she buys a 25¢, how much change will she get? **75¢**
5. If she buys a 60¢, how much change will she get? **40¢**
6. If she buys a 45¢, how much change will she get? **55¢**
7. If she buys a 15¢, how much change will she get? **85¢**
8. If she buys a 30¢, how much change will she get? **70¢**

PAGE 42

More Money

Count the money and write the amount for each.

$1.45 $1.20
$1.00   60¢ or $0.60
$2.10 $2.25

PAGE 43

Do You Have Enough?

Circle the answer to each question.

1. Do you have enough to buy this? 99¢ — **yes** / no
2. Do you have enough to buy this? $2.00 — **yes** / no
3. Do you have enough to buy this? $1.50 — yes / **no**
4. Do you have enough to buy this? 55¢ — **yes** / no

PAGE 44

Total It Up

Write the total amount the two items would cost together.

$1.25 + $1.50 = **$2.75**
50¢ + 26¢ = **76¢**
$8.50 + $7.00 = **$15.50**
$5.50 + $4.00 = **$9.50**

PAGE 45

How Much Money?

Count and write the amount.

25 50 75 85 90 95 **95** ¢
25 50 60 65 70 75 **75** ¢
50 75 85 95 1.00 $ **1** . **00**
5 6 6.25 6.50 6.55 $ **6** . **55**
10 15 16 16.25 16.35 $ **16** . **35**

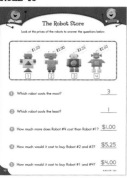

PAGE 46

The Robot Store

Look at the prices of the robots to answer the questions below.

1. $1.50   2. $1.00   3. $3.25   4. $2.50

1. Which robot costs the most? **3**
2. Which robot costs the least? **1**
3. How much more does Robot #4 cost than Robot #1? **$1.00**
4. How much would it cost to buy Robot #2 and #3? **$5.25**
5. How much would it cost to buy Robot #1 and #4? **$4.00**

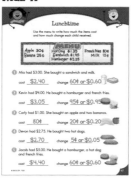

PAGE 47

Lunchtime

Use the menu to write how much the items cost and how much change each child received.

MENU
Apple 30¢   Hot Dog $1.35   French Fries 80¢
Banana 25¢   Sandwich $1.95   Milk 15¢
Hamburger $2.25

1. Mia had $3.00. She bought a sandwich and milk.
   cost **$2.40**   change **60¢ or $0.60**
2. Kevin had $4.00. He bought a hamburger and french fries.
   cost **$3.05**   change **95¢ or $0.95**
3. Carly had $1.00. She bought an apple and two bananas.
   cost **80¢**   change **20¢ or $0.20**
4. Devon had $2.75. He bought two hot dogs.
   cost **$2.70**   change **5¢ or $0.05**
5. Jacob had $5.00. He bought a hamburger, a hot dog and french fries.
   cost **$4.40**   change **60¢ or $0.60**

PAGE 48

Toy Snakes

Write > or < to show which toy snake costs more.

$3.95 **>** $3.40
$6.25 **>** $5.00
75¢ **<** $1.00
$2.75 **>** $2.50
$1.25 **>** 25¢

PAGE 49

Money

Count the money and write the amount for each.

50¢ or $0.50   30¢ or $0.30
25¢ or $0.25   55¢ or $0.55
$3.25 $3.06

PAGE 50

Heads or Tails?

Write **penny**, **nickel**, **dime**, or **quarter** and its value next to each coin.

	dime	10 ¢
	quarter	25 ¢
	penny	1 ¢
	nickel	5 ¢
	nickel	5 ¢
	penny	1 ¢
	dime	10 ¢
	quarter	25 ¢

PAGE 51

If You Had $100

Draw a picture of what you would buy if you had $100.

Answers will vary